LET IT RIP!

Welcome to the Beyblade Metal Fusion Annual. Here you will find all of the information you need to know about our hero, Gingka, his loyal group of friends and their enemy the Dark Nebula. Plus there are four fascinating stories about their adventures and battles! Keep an eye out for top battling tips and the chance to design your very own Beyblade.

As well as character profiles and entertaining episodes, you'll find plenty of teasing activities to test the knowledge of even the most obsessive Beyblade fan.

There are plenty of questions in the pages ahead but one of the most intriguing answers will be whether Gingka can find the bravery and strength to defend his impressive Blading record and the honour of Beyblade.
Remember, it's not just the power of the top, it's also the spirit of the Beyblader that matters... 3, 2, 1 – LET IT RIP!

CONTENTS

Pedigree®

Published 2011.
Pedigree Books Ltd, Beech Hill House,
Walnut Gardens, Exeter, Devon EX4 4DH
books@pedigreegroup.co.uk | www.pedigreebooks.com

NELVANA
A Corus® Entertainment Inc. Company

d-rights

£7.99

GINGKA

Gingka is the hero of the Beyblade story. He is very skilled and never turns down a good battle, travelling from city to city looking for his next Beyblade challenge

Gingka settles in one of the towns he visits and befriends a young Beyblader called Kenta and a Bey mechanic called Madoka.

Living by the words of his father, who told him that a Beyblader's true strength is drawn from his spirit, Gingka displays awesome dedication and knowledge of Beyblade.

BEYBLADE:
STORM PEGASUS

Haunted by a hidden past, Gingka is fuelled by a secret purpose that drives him to be better and stronger at Beyblade. The Dark Nebula, an evil group, have targeted Gingka and want to destroy our hero as they know that he is the person standing in the way of their plans – the unleashing of an evil and forbidden Beyblade.

SPECIAL MOVES:

Pegasus Starblast Attack, Pegasus Tornado Wing, Meteor Shower Attack, Pegasus Storm Bringer.

KYOYA

Kyoya was once the callous leader of the Face Hunters – a neighbourhood gang that bullies the weak, stealing their Beyblade points after forcing them into illegal battles. Kyoya's Rock Leone Bey is a Defence Type and he uses natural conditions like the power of the wind to help him win.

Kyoya's best friend is Benkei, who started to follow Kyoya after losing several battles to him.

BEYBLADE:
ROCK LEONE

After being influenced by Gingka, Kyoya realised how meaningless and destructive his way of life was. Putting his past behind him, Kyoya eventually joined Gingka in the fight against the Dark Nebula.

SPECIAL MOVES:

Lion Gale-force Wall, Lion 100 Fang Fury, Lion Wild Wind Fang Dance, King Lion Tearing Blast.

BENKEI

The brute with a heart, Benkei started off as a Face Hunter loyally following Kyoya and doing a lot of his dirty work by forcing younger, weaker Beybladers into battle where Kyoya and the other Face Hunters are able to gain many points.

Benkei continues to follow Kyoya but now they have turned their backs on a destructive past and are determined to defend the good guys.

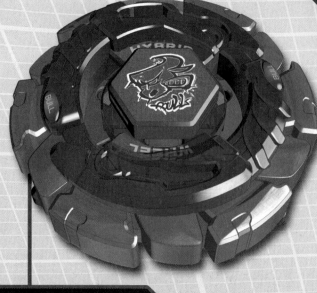

BEYBLADE:

DARK BULL

He is surprised and touched that the people he used to pick on, like Gingka and Kenta, are now the ones there to help him when he's down.

SPECIAL MOVES:

Dark Bull Red-horn Uppercut, Bull Uppercut, Tornado Bull Uppercut.

KENTA

Kenta loves to Beyblade and he and his friends always practise and battle whenever and wherever they can. When the Face Hunters confronted Kenta and forced him to battle, Gingka heroically came to his rescue and the two began a loyal friendship.

Kenta tries as hard as he can to learn the craft and, after seeing Gingka in battle, he sought his mentorship and asked for as many coaching tips as possible. But Kenta isn't the only one to benefit from the relationship; as Gingka teaches Kenta about the secrets of Beyblade, Kenta shows him the strength of friendship.

BEYBLADE:

FLAME SAGITTARIO

SPECIAL MOVES:

Sagittario Flame Claw.

Madoka is a Beyblade mechanic. She doesn't participate in the action but knows all there is to know about Beyblade. Madoka has her own workshop, tools and analysers to repair and optimise Beyblades. She also helps her friends prepare and plan strategies for battling opponents.

Her father owns a Beyblade shop and, although she's obsessed with Beyblading, Madoka doesn't really enjoy battling, preferring to concentrate on strategy and taking care of battered Beys, repairing when possible.

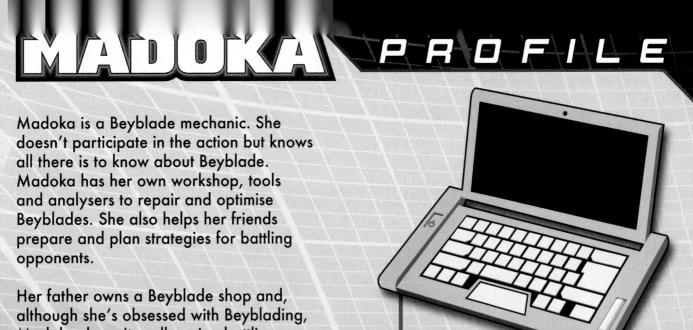

TOOL:

LAPTOP

SPECIAL MOVES:

Computers, mechanics and also very knowledgeable about Beyblades.

RYUGA

Ryuga is the leader of the Dark Nebula and an enemy of Gingka. After laying in a coma for years, Ryuga was stirred by the presence of Gingka and Pegasus at his doorstep and unexpectedly awoke. A vicious and merciless character, Ryuga gathers strength by sucking the power from his opponent's Beyblades. His goal is to restore his L-Drago to full power and unleash its evil on the world.

BEYBLADE:
LIGHTNING L-DRAGO

SPECIAL MOVES:

Dragon Emperor Soaring Bite Strike.

11

DOJI

Doji is an executive of the Dark Nebula – an organisation determined to take over the world of Beyblade. They plan to unleash a long forbidden Beyblade as part of their evil scheme. With Gingka and his Beyblade being the one thing standing in Doji's way, he plans to destroy them.

Doji is first revealed when he confronts Kyoya, challenging him to a battle and insisting that the leader of the Face Hunters helps him in his quest to defeat Gingka. Doji also presented Benkei with his Dark Bull Beyblade.

BEYBLADE:

DARK WOLF

SPECIAL MOVES:

Darkness Howling Blazer.

12

WATCH OUT FOR...

PROFILES

Beyblade Metal Fusion fans will come across a number of characters during various adventures, here are a few important ones you need to know about!

RYO

Gingka's father originally held the Bey Pegasus before being defeated by Ryuga and lightning L-Drago. Ryo's final words to his son were to defeat Ryuga so he can return L-Drago to its rightful place.

HIKARU

Hikaru made a vow to her mother years ago that she would become the best blader in the world, but knows she must defeat Gingka to do so.

HYOMA

Hyoma is an old friend of Gingka's who tests the character of both Gingka and Kyoya before allowing them entrance to Koma Village.

YU

A new kid on the scene, Yu causes a stir when he defeats Gingka at Battle Beybladers.

TSUBASA

A new rival to Gingka, Tsubasa tests his strength and teaches him some tricks of the trade.

HOKUTO

A wise talking dog who is an old friend of Gingka's and helps in his quest to find a scroll that could provide more power for Pegasus.

SORA

A Beyblader with amazing power but no control, Sora tries to copy Gingka's special move but cannot pull it off.

TERU

Now a Beyblader, Teru used to be a talented dancer until being involved in an onstage accident. When he was bed-ridden and recovering, Teru was inspired to become a Beyblader after watching Gingka on TV.

BUSUJIMA

A gang leader, Busujima's group have taken over a stadium in a ghost town.

WATARIGANI

A crab-obsessed villain who challenges Gingka to a battle, forcing him to fight after kidnapping Madoka and refusing to release her until the battle takes place.

DAN and REIKI

A brotherly twin duo who are friends with Kenta.

PEGASUS HAS LANDED

Kenta and his friends were taking part in the WBBA competition, trying to earn as many Beyblade points as possible.

Meanwhile, Gingka was walking through town when he saw two Beyblader fans rushing to the stadium. Rather than taking part, Gingka decided to rest up and save his energy for the bigger battles ahead and fell asleep, with his trusty Storm Pegasus Bey on a nearby roof overlooking the city.

"Go Sagittario!" Kenta shouted as his favourite Beyblade spun against an opponent's.

Kenta's friends had already been knocked out of the competition but were supporting him with great enthusiasm inside the stadium.

After some successful battles Kenta was eventually defeated and crashed out of the competition. Kenta and his friends left the stadium, discussing their performances.

"Oh, after all that I only got into the top eight," Kenta sighed.

"Last time we watched you didn't even make it to the third round," his friend replied, trying to encourage Kenta. "At least you're getting a little better."

Kenta's other friend had some words of advice: "Next time you should try using my Beyblade. You could get a lot further using an Attack Type."

Kenta defended his own Beyblade, insisting that he wanted to get stronger with Sagittario, a Stamina Type, as he believed they make a good team. All three friends agreed that it doesn't mean anything unless you can win with your own Bey and that the only way to get better is to practise.

They planned to have one more battle… until they saw how dark it was outside and realised it was later than they thought!

Running home, dreaming of becoming the number one Beyblader, Kenta bumped into the imposing figure of Benkei and some other Face Hunters.

"What's your problem?" Benkei bellowed, as Kenta looked up at him from the floor. "I'm sorry, I didn't do it on purpose," Kenta pleaded.

"To make up for it you can battle Mr Benkei," said one of the Face Hunters. "When you lose, we get all your points!"

Realising exactly who he had come across, Kenta knew that he could be about to lose all of his hard-earned points.

"No way, you can't have all my Beyblade points. If you want them just enter a face-off and win them fairly. That's how it's done."

Kenta tried to run away but found himself surrounded by Face Hunters.

"If you don't want to lose, all you've got to do is beat Benkei," said one of the Hunters. Realising he'd been backed into a corner Kenta shouted for help.

Gingka was close by but he was fast asleep!

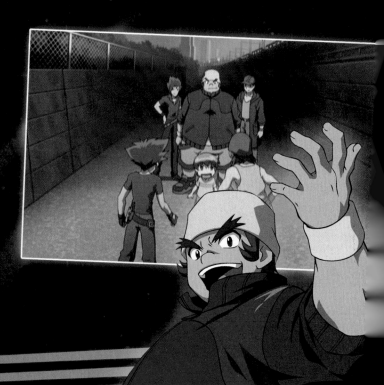

"Yell all you want, no-one is coming to help you," Benkei sneered. "Alright, let's get ready to battle."

Kenta protested saying he didn't want to fight that kind of battle, but he had no choice.

"3, 2, 1... Let it Rip," one of the Face Hunters shouted as Benkei released his Bey with great power and Kenta begrudgingly launched his in response.

It wasn't long before Kenta's Bey slowed down.

view, knocking the Face Hunter's top away into the air before it came to a standstill on the ground in front of Benkei.

"What?" Benkei shouted. "But how?"
He looked around to see a tall, slim figure with bright red hair and a long white scarf.

"Beyblading is supposed to fun. You gang up on someone; you're not a true Beyblader!," he said.

"My grandma spins harder than that!" Benkei mocked.

"Come on Sagittario!" Kenta shouted, realising that his Beyblade was taking a pummelling.

"Who do you think you are?" asked Benkei.
"The name's Gingka, Gingka Hagane," replied the stranger.

Benkei launched his final attack as his Bey spun and fizzed straight for Sagittario. It looked as though Benkei's Beyblade was about to smash into Kenta's until an even faster, bright blue Bey came spinning into

A fuming Benkei suggested it was not very wise for anybody to interrupt him during battle and challenged Gingka.

"No problem, big guy," answered Gingka.

"This is going to be a handicap match... one versus five," one of the Face Hunters announced.
Despite Kenta's protests that it wasn't a fair battle, Gingka decided to take on the Face Hunters' challenge.

As all five of the Face Hunters' Bey's were launched, Gingka released his Storm Pegasus Bey at great speed.

"Wow it's too fast. I can't even see the Bey," shouted an excited Kenta as Storm Pegasus smashed through every one of the rival Beys. The Face Hunters couldn't believe Gingka's impressive standard and Kenta was in awe of his new friend's abilities.

Later that evening Kenta and Gingka walked through the city as Kenta kept thanking his new friend for helping. Gingka wanted to know who Benkei was and Kenta explained he was part of the Face Hunters, an evil gang who forced younger opponents into battles to steal their points.
Gingka wasn't surprised. He suggested that thugs like the Face Hunters were everywhere. He then explained to Kenta that he was

travelling the country searching for stronger enemie's in order to become the strongest Beyblader. An impressed Kenta asked Gingka how he too could become a stronger Beyblader. But Gingka explained that there was much more to Blading than just strength.

"It takes a lot of heart," Gingka explained as he instructed Kenta to relax as he lay down on the grass.

They both looked into the night sky and Gingka continued to tell Kenta his theories on Beyblading.

"A Bey's true strength has nothing to do with attack power or stamina. It attacks using the feelings of the Beyblader that's connected with it, as if all the power in the cosmos was being poured into it," said Gingka.
"You must put your heart that is as big as the starry sky into it."

Gingka soon fell asleep and Kenta decided it was time he went home.

Back at the Face Hunters' warehouse, Benkei and his friends were being lectured by Kyoya, their callous leader, who was not impressed by their defeat to Gingka.

"So, you got your butts kicked and then you just came crying back here like little babies?' he fumed.

Benkei explained that Gingka was too strong but suggested that if Kyoya faced him he could crush Gingka's Storm Pegasus with his Rock Leone.

"How dare you speak the name of Leone without my permission," blasted Kyoya.

He ordered Benkei to 'man-up' and take care of Gingka. "Just do whatever you have to do," he said.

The next morning, Gingka was rudely awoken by the Face Hunters and invited to take part in another battle.

He just missed an excited Kenta who had run all the way from home to meet up with him. A disappointed Kenta believed Gingka had left for a new town and was sad at losing what he'd hoped would be a new friend. He decided to search around town for Gingka.

Kenta spotted the Face Hunters walking towards an empty building site where he discovered Gingka surrounded by more Face Hunters, including Benkei. Kyoya was watching the action from distance.

"Gingka Hagane, you thought you were pretty clever embarrassing us yesterday," said Benkei. "So today we're going to return the favour with the Face Hunters' speciality… The 100 Bey battle!"

Benkei was excited by the battle and started shouting about how the Beys were bouncing into each other, increasing their power and changing their trajectory so they could attack from all directions.

Kenta pleaded with them to stop and urged Gingka to run.

"I'm not going anywhere," stated Gingka, as he prepared to launch Storm Pegasus.

"Let's roll. It's show-time Storm Pegasus," Gingka shouted. "Let it rip!"

Gingka accepted the challenge and within seconds one hundred Beyblades were flying towards him.

"This does not look good!" shouted Kenta, as he saw one hundred Bey's spinning and bouncing off each other in front of Gingka.

Storm Pegasus flew through the air at an incredible pace, spinning at the speed of a tornado and sending all one hundred of the Face Hunters' Beyblades out of control.

"The difference between winning and losing is the Bey's spirit," announced Gingka as he triumphantly held Storm Pegasus in the air.

Then a voice made both Gingka and Kenta turn around.

"At last it seems that an opponent worthy of me and my Rock Leone has made himself known." It was Kyoya.

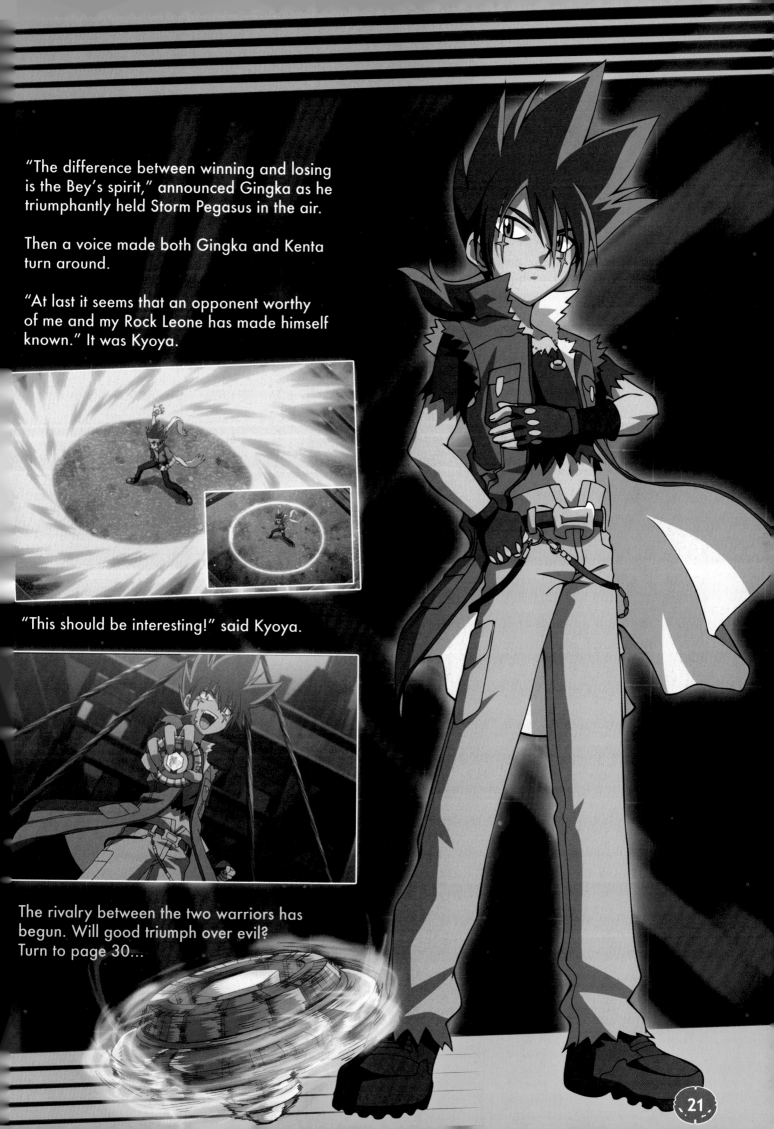

"This should be interesting!" said Kyoya.

The rivalry between the two warriors has begun. Will good triumph over evil?
Turn to page 30...

MEMORY QUIZ

QUESTION 1:

What is the name of the competition that Kenta takes part in at the beginning of the first episode?

Answer:

QUESTION 2:

What is the name of Kenta's Bey?

Answer:

QUESTION 3:

Does Kenta finish in the top five of the competition or the top eight?

Answer:

QUESTION 4:

Who bumps into Kenta whilst he's walking home, knocking him to the ground?

Answer:

QUESTION 5:

Who comes to Kenta's rescue after he's ambushed by the Face Hunters?

Answer:

QUESTION 6:

What is Gingka's last name?

Answer:

QUESTION 7:

How many Face Hunters does Gingka confront in his first battle against the bad guys?

Answer:

QUESTION 8:

What is the name of Kyoya's Beyblade?

Answer:

QUESTION 9:

Gingka is invited to take on the Face Hunters in another battle, but against a lot more. How many Face Hunters does he take on?

Answer:

QUESTION 10:

After defeating the Face Hunters what does Gingka say is the difference between winning and losing?

Answer:

ANSWERS ON PAGE 78

RULES RECAP

YOU MAY BE NEW TO THE WORLD OF BEYBLADE OR YOU COULD BE AN EXPERIENCED AND BATTLE-HARDENED BLADER. EITHER WAY A QUICK CHECK OF THE RULES OF BEYBLADE WON'T DO YOU ANY HARM!

GOAL

To be the first player to score seven or more points.

HOW TO BATTLE

- All official Beyblade battles begin with the signal: "3,2,1 – LET IT RIP!"
- At the signal, both Bey's are launched into the Beystadium arena.
- There is one launch per battle and the battle ends when one top is left standing.

SCORING

- If your top spins longer than your opponent's you score 1 point.
- If you touch your opponent during his launch you lose 1 point.
- If you fail to launch your top successfully into the arena your opponent scores 1 point.
- If your top gets trapped in a penalty pocket, your opponent scores 2 points.
- If you touch the arena during battle your opponent scores 3 points and that battle is immediately over.
- You should compete in multiple battles until one player scores 7 or more points!

QUICK PLAY

For faster competitions try...

Best of Three Knockout: The first player to win two battles (by out-spinning or knocking out his opponent) wins the competition.

Triple Shot: A best of three contest in which the players choose a different top for each round. Players decide beforehand which tops will battle each other.

Last Man Standing: Multiple players battle it out at the same time and the last top standing is the winner.

QUICK ACTIVITY

Who am I?
Clue: My Beyblade is Storm Pegasus, I wear a white scarf and one of my special moves is Pegasus Tornado Wing.

Answer:

BUMPER
BEYBLADE
WORDSEARCH

SCAN THROUGH THIS GRID OF LETTERS AND TRY TO FIND AS MANY OF THE BEYBLADE HEROES AND VILLAINS AS YOU CAN. THE NAMES COULD BE WRITTEN HORIZONTALLY. VERTICALLY. DIAGONALLY AND BACKWARDS OR FORWARDS, SO YOU'LL NEED TO KEEP YOUR EYES PEELED. CHECK OUT THE LIST OF NAMES BELOW AND SEE IF YOU CAN FIND THEM ALL!

N	B	E	N	Y	I	O	L	I	S	O	G	A
P	G	D	Z	U	R	G	J	J	N	B	C	Q
E	I	G	V	J	K	O	D	P	O	E	C	B
O	N	X	Z	S	D	A	Y	O	Y	K	S	E
B	G	T	S	J	K	B	L	P	W	T	A	N
R	K	V	H	O	K	U	T	O	W	O	U	K
O	A	B	H	K	I	U	A	Y	U	F	C	E
A	A	A	S	A	B	U	S	T	J	U	S	I
Z	J	V	F	G	Y	T	T	S	N	L	A	S
O	B	N	K	I	D	F	Y	Z	K	E	N	G
T	Y	S	J	F	T	O	B	I	O	G	K	A
E	P	R	W	D	C	G	S	O	X	Z	G	F
R	M	Y	G	R	F	C	X	S	D	U	Z	A
U	K	A	M	O	Y	H	T	E	Y	R	K	R
L	C	F	G	J	N	S	D	R	A	W	O	O
R	M	A	D	O	K	A	D	L	I	M	O	S

- GINGKA
- KENTA
- DOJI
- TOBIO
- SORA
- KYOYA
- MADOKA
- RYO
- TSUBASA
- TERU
- BENKEI
- RYUGA
- HYOMA
- HOKUTO
- YU

MEGA MAZE

START

KYOYA HAS BEEN TRAPPED IN THIS MAZE BY DOJI, WHO HAS ALSO HIDDEN HIS BEYBLADE, ROCK LEONE. FIRSTLY DRAW A LINE TO GUIDE KYOYA TO HIS BEYBLADE BEFORE DRAWING ANOTHER ONE TO HELP HIM ESCAPE THE MAZE AND JOIN-UP WITH HIS FRIEND GINGKA. WATCH OUT FOR SEVERAL DEAD ENDS ALONG THE WAY!

ROCK LEONE

FINISH

27

BEYBLADE
MATCH-UP

ALL OF THE GOODIES AND BADDIES HAVE JUMBLED UP THEIR BEYBLADES. USE YOUR EXPERT KNOWLEDGE TO RETURN EACH BEYBLADE TO ITS RIGHTFUL OWNER BY DRAWING A LINE TO MATCH THEM UP.

GINGKA

KYOYA

BENKEI

KENTA

RYUGA

DOJI

DARK WOLF

LIGHTENING
L-DRAGO

FLAME
SAGITTARIO

ROCK LEONE

STORM
PEGASUS

DARK BULL

ANSWERS ON PAGE 78

BEYBLADE
TOP TYPES

EVERY BEYBLADE TOP BELONGS TO ONE OF FOUR COMBAT CATEGORIES, WHICH ARE BASED ON ITS PRIMARY BATTLE STRENGTH. THEY ARE...

ATTACK

Attack Types move quickly around the stadium, hitting with power. They behave aggressively, tracking and attacking their opponent.

DEFENCE

Defence Types are strong and sturdy. Their solid construction is designed to ward off attacks and maintain a stationary, stable position in battle.

STAMINA

Stamina Types are built to spin longer and outlast an opponent. They can even out-spin a steady Defence Type.

BALANCE

Balance Types combine the qualities of Attack, Balance and Defence types and usually incorporate design elements from all three.

QUICK ACTIVITY

Who am I?
Clue: My Beyblade is Rock Leone, I have been a Face Hunter and one of my special moves is Lion Gale-Force Wall.

Answer:

29

Gingka showed off his Blading skills to Kenta and some of his friends, who were clearly impressed.

"Yo Kenta, where did you meet such an amazing Beyblader?" asked one of the crowd.

Kenta told how Gingka took on one hundred Face Hunters and beat them, and suddenly all of the young Beybladers crowded around. In the background, a young girl watched as Gingka gave tips and advice about how to be a good Beyblader.

Meanwhile, at the Face Hunters' hideout, Kyoya demanded that each of his bullies continued to battle him, despite their tiredness.

"Prepare for battle," he shouted to Benkei. "I'm not pumped enough yet!"

Kyoya unleashed his feared Bey, Rock Leone, as he continued to prepare for his much-anticipated battle against Gingka. After defeating all of his gang, Kyoya laughed loudly and claimed he was going to "crush Gingka, like the little bug that he is."

Gingka and Kenta were relaxing and chatting about the town when Gingka revealed, much to Kenta's delight, that he was going to stick around for a while.

"I've found a really strong opponent here," Gingka said, referring to Kyoya.

Kenta was worried and explained how Kyoya's Rock Leone was extremely strong and that he never stopped until an opponent was completely destroyed.

"They say Kyoya's Rock Leone is like a wild animal enjoying the hunt," Kenta warned.

"Look Kenta, I'm travelling to meet opponents like that. I really need the challenge," replied Gingka.

"It's ok," he reassured his new friend. "No matter who I battle, I fancy my chances, as long as I've got Pegasus."

Gingka and Kenta were interrupted by the young girl who had watched them earlier.

"Pegasus... poor thing," she said.

Holding out a small computer she scanned both Gingka and Pegasus, looking for signs of damage.

"Just as I thought, several joints have some wear. This will cause a slight calculation error in its overall balance," she added.

The young girl explained about further scratch damage and how it could harm the performance of Gingka's Storm Pegasus. She then offered to treat its injuries.

"Until then, no battling, ok?" she stated.

"Ok," replied Gingka. "But who are you anyway?"

She took Gingka and Kenta to her father's Beyblade store and explained how she used the basement as her Beyblade workshop area.

Revealing that she chose not to battle very often and enjoyed fixing Beys and doing battle simulations, the girl introduced herself as Madoka.

Madoka took Pegasus and placed it in a special computer.

"This is more serious than I first thought," she said. "It's not just the cracks, there is a lot of debris stuck inside."

Madoka sprayed Pegasus to remove the debris, and explained how it could have an effect on the balance of the Bey.

"Everyone always focuses so much on the battle that they forget to stop and think about their own precious Bey," Madoka said. She added that Pegasus would have to stay the night for the necessary repairs.

Gingka made himself comfortable on the sofa for the night as he couldn't bear to be away from his treasured Pegasus.

Kenta asked Madoka to take a look at his Sagittario too.

As Gingka lay on the sofa watching Madoka tend to Pegasus he considered his new friend's actions, realising that being a great Beyblader isn't just about battling, it's more than that.

The next morning, Kenta ran to the store to see how Madoka had got on fixing Pegasus – but on his way there he was again ambushed by Benkei, who tripped him up and grabbed the flailing Sagittario out of the air.

"This guy really is a clutz!" Benkei smiled.

"What are you doing, you Face Stealing monster, give me my Sagittario back," pleaded Kenta.

"If you want it back you have to bring Gingka to Metal Tower," Benkei insisted.

The Face Hunters ran off with Sagittario and Kenta rushed to tell Gingka. Both Beybladers decided to head for Metal Tower.

"Hold on!" cried Madoka. "I still haven't finished Pegasus's maintenance yet. I have to fine tune its balance."

"We don't have time for that now," replied Gingka. "Man up Kenta."

"Argh... boys," growled Madoka as she chased after Gingka and Kenta.

They arrived at Metal Tower to see Benkei and the other Face Hunters waiting for them.

"Give me back my Sagittario!" demanded Kenta.

"Sure," replied Benkei. "Just as soon as Gingka defeats Kyoya in a battle!"

"Any day of the week buddy," answered Gingka. "Where's he hiding, behind your skirt?"

"You're worst nightmare is right here," announced Kyoya as he appeared from behind the other Face Hunters. "Let's do this right now."

Just as Gingka was about to accept the challenge, Madoka burst in, protesting that Pegasus wasn't battle ready. Gingka thought he had no choice, particularly when he saw Benkei dangling Kenta's Sagittario from the top of the tower.

"If you won't fight, I'll drop the Bey," threatened Benkei.

Gingka knew he had to fight.

"Sorry Pegasus," he said. "Please do your best for just this one battle."

Madoka pleaded with Gingka. He explained that whilst Pegasus was everything to him, Sagittario meant everything to Kenta and he couldn't let his friend's Bey be destroyed.

The rivals prepared for battle. "3,2,1... Let it rip," they both shouted, launching their Beys into the circle.

Kyoya's Rock Leone spun in the middle, not attacking Pegasus. Kenta wondered what the Face Hunter had up his sleeve.

Madoka opened up her laptop and checked out Rock Leone and realised it was the ideal Defence Type.

"But you can't win if you don't attack, right?" asked Kenta.

"Somehow I have a bad feeling about this," Madoka replied.

Gingka launched his first attack but Pegasus was repelled by Leone. He tried another attack.

"You ain't seen nothing yet," mocked Kyoya. "Roar Leone," he shouted as his Bey started to blow Pegasus away with ease.

Madoka realised that Kyoya was using the strong winds at the top of the tower to increase the power and speed of his Beyblade.

"Twisted, he lured Gingka into a trap and chose a location that works to his advantage," said Kenta.

"Wise up Gingka," shouted Kyoya. "You should know what it takes to win a battle; the Beyblader's skills, the Bey's ability and how well a chosen battle location fits your purpose."

Kyoya prepared Leone for its special move, Lion Gale-Force Wall, as Pegasus appeared to be swallowed up by the wind.

Gingka pleaded with his Bey to hang on, realising that if Kyoya attacked, Pegasus could lose in a stadium out.

If he didn't attack he knew that Pegasus would be the one to finish first. What could he do?

"Think all day, the answer is still the same," gloated Kyoya. "You're toast."

Kyoya looked like winning. But Gingka battled on.

The wind was so strong that it sucked Gingka's scarf into the sky. He decided it was time to attack Leone. Pegasus crashed into Leone and spun into the air as Kyoya claimed the win due to a stadium out.

Kenta burst into tears. He apologised to Gingka for having to put Pegasus at risk, but his friend had a confident grin on his face.

"My Pegasus hasn't been beaten yet buddy," he said as Pegasus flew back down towards the stadium crashing into Leone.

"Pegasus Star Blast Attack!" shouted Gingka, as his Bey knocked Leone away for a stadium out to seal victory for the good guys.

The Face Hunters and Kyoya were astounded. Gingka and his friends celebrated an unlikely victory.

Kyoya realised that Gingka was always one step ahead of him, planning for a battle like this and waiting for the eye of the storm, for the fastest wind and the best time to attack.

Madoka analysed the tactics that Gingka used and showed Kenta.

Benkei dropped Sagittario in amazement and it rolled straight to Gingka who returned the Bey to Kenta.

A grateful Kenta thanked both Gingka and Pegasus. They were joined by Madoka and the friends walked away from the tower.

Madoka scolded Gingka for being so reckless with Pegasus and insisted that he apologised to his Bey, which he begrudgingly did.

Back at his hideout, Kyoya couldn't believe that he'd been defeated. He was taking out his anger on the other Face Hunters until somebody interrupted him.

"Do you want to win against Gingka Hagane?" a voice asked from the shadows. "Do you want to become even stronger?"

"Who the heck are you?" Benkei asked.

"How about I grant that wish for you?" offered the stranger standing in the shadows, as he let out a frightening laugh.

Who is this stranger? Can he really help Kyoya defeat Gingka? Turn to page 46.

BATTLE OF THE BEYBLADES

YOU'VE LEARNED MORE ABOUT OUR HEROES, THE ART OF BEYBLADING AND HOW TO LOOK AFTER YOUR BEYS. NOW YOUR BEYBLADE KNOWLEDGE WILL BE PUT TO THE TEST IN THIS BOARD GAME FULL OF BEYBLADE TEASERS.

AS MANY PLAYERS AS YOU LIKE CAN TAKE PART AND YOU CAN USE YOUR BEYS AS COUNTERS. YOU WILL ALSO NEED A DICE. PUT ALL OF THE BEYS ON THE STARTING SPACE AND TAKE TURNS TO THROW THE DICE TO SEE WHO GETS THE HIGHEST NUMBER. WHOEVER GETS THE HIGHEST SCORE GOES FIRST AND THEN GO CLOCKWISE IN THE DIRECTION OF HOW YOU ARE SITTING TO DECIDE WHO GOES NEXT.

THE WINNER IS THE FIRST BEY TO REACH THE FINISHING LINE! 3-2-1... LET IT RIP!

START
1

2
You won an epic battle! - Move forward two spaces!

3

7
You lost three battles in a row! Go backwards 4 spaces!

6
You're Bey has been maintained very well, Madoka will be pleased - Move forward three spaces!

5
Have another go!

4
You miss-shot during battle - Miss a turn!

8
You gave a friend some good coaching tips - Have another go!

9

10
What is the name of Gingka's Bey? If you get it right move forward one space, if you get it wrong go back a space!

11

16
Name two characters that have been Face Hunters. If you get them both right move forward two spaces, if not, go back two spaces!

17
What is Kenta's Beyblade called? If you get it right move forward 1 space, if you get it wrong go back 3 spaces!

26
What Type of Bey is Kenta's Sagittario? If you get it right move forward 1 space, if you get it wrong go back to square 13!

27
Move forward 1 space!

15
Have another go!

18

25
Go back 2 spaces!

28

14
Roll the dice again – If you get an even number move forward that many spaces, but if you get an odd number, move back that many spaces!

19
Miss a go!

24
Whose Bey is called Rock Leone? If you get it right move forward 1 space, if you get it wrong go back 3 spaces!

29
Go back 3 spaces!

13
Miss a go!

20
Have another go!

23

FINISH 30

12
Kyoya defeated you in an important battle – Go back three spaces!

21
Roll the dice again. If you roll a one then you have to move back to the start of the game!

22
Your Bey managed to withstand a Bull Uppercut attack from Benkei's Dark Bull Bey! Move forward 2 spaces!

39

BATTLE TIPS

GREAT BEYBLADE PLAYERS COMBINE GOOD TECHNIQUE WITH A SMART LAUNCH. IF YOU'RE STRUGGLING TO WIN OR JUST TRYING TO PERFECT YOUR STYLE, WHY NOT TRY OUT THESE TIPS?

CONCEALMENT LAUNCH

Position your launcher low, behind one of the Beystadium walls. Pull the ripcord really hard and lift the launcher so that the Bey just clears the wall and lands in the middle of the arena. Your opponent won't see where it's going to land until it's too late. The top will tend to land lightly, stay in one place and spin for ages! This technique is most effective with Stamina Types.

RICOCHET LAUNCH

Launch the top sideways into the arena by pulling along the ripcord instead of pulling the ripcord itself and aim for the wall. If this is done correctly, the top will hit the wall hard and rebound into a fierce attack. This could smash your opponent's top or knock it into a pocket. This technique works well with Defence Types.

SHIELD LAUNCH

Angle your Bey so it's aligned with the slope of the arena wall and then launch. Landing at the same angle creates greater spin velocity and if your Bey is hit within the first few seconds of battle it will absorb the blow. This technique should work well with any type.

THE SHARPSHOOTER

Aim your launch so that your top hits your opponent's before it lands. When done well, this launch can cause major damage to opposing tops and can work well with any type.

QUICK ACTIVITY

Who am I?
Clue: My Beyblade is Dark Bull, I loyally follow Kyoya and one of my special moves is the Bull Uppercut.

Answer:

MIXED-UP CHARACTERS

THE NAMES OF THESE BEYBLADE CHARACTERS HAVE SPUN OUT OF CONTROL AND BEEN COMPLETELY MIXED UP INTO ANAGRAMS. CAN YOU USE YOUR EXPERT BEYBLADER KNOWLEDGE TO WORK OUT WHO'S WHO?

KANGIG

Answer:

AROS

Answer:

TENKA

Answer:

YAKYO

Answer:

JODI

Answer:

KAMADO

Answer:

OBOIT

Answer:

ENEKBI

Answer:

ANSWERS ON PAGE 78

41

BEY BRAIN TEASER

LET IT RIP!

SO YOU THINK YOU KNOW YOUR BEYBLADE FACTS AND STATISTICS? WELL PUT YOURSELF TO THE TEST BY ANSWERING THESE 20 TEASING QUESTIONS IN THE BEYBLADE QUIZ. TRY TO REMEMBER ALL OF THE ANSWERS WITHOUT USING ANY OF THE OTHER ANNUAL PAGES FOR CLUES. IF YOU WANT TO MAKE IT EVEN HARDER, THEN WHY NOT GIVE YOURSELF A TIME LIMIT? GRAB A WATCH OR CLOCK AND GIVE YOURSELF TWO MINUTES TO ANSWER AS MANY QUESTIONS AS YOU CAN...

QUESTION 1:

What is Gingka's Beyblade called?
Answer:

QUESTION 2:

Name one of Kyoya's special moves?
Answer:

QUESTION 3:

Which Beyblader used to be a talented dancer before an on-stage accident?
Answer:

QUESTION 4:

Who uses a Beyblade called Lightning L-Drago?
Answer:

QUESTION 5:

Who is the Beyblade mechanic?
Answer:

QUESTION 6:

Who got a hot dog instead of a burger?
Answer:

QUESTION 7:

Who tests Ginga and Kyoya before allowing them entry to Koma Village?
Answer:

QUESTION 8:

What is Benkei's Beyblade called?
Answer:

QUESTION 9:

Doji is an executive of the Dark what?

Answer:

QUESTION 10:

Name the character that matches this description: A wise talking dog.

Answer:

QUESTION 11:

Who uses a Beyblade called Rock Leone?

Answer:

QUESTION 12:

What is the name of Gingka's father?

Answer:

QUESTION 13:

Who is the leader of the Dark Nebula?

Answer:

QUESTION 14:

What is the name of Reiki's brother?

Answer:

QUESTION 15:

What is Kenta's special move called?

Answer:

QUESTION 16:

Name one of Gingka's special moves

Answer:

QUESTION 17:

Whose special move is the Darkness Howling Blazer?

Answer:

QUESTION 18:

What colour is Kenta's hair?

Answer:

QUESTION 19:

What is the name of the crab-obsessed villain who kidnaps Madoka?

Answer:

QUESTION 20:

Whose special move is the Dragon Emperor Soaring Bite Strike?

Answer:

ANSWERS ON PAGE 78

BATTLE RECORD

DATE OF BATTLE	OPPONENT	LOCATION

LEAGUE TABLE - GIVE YOURSELF, YOUR FRIENDS AND OPPONENTS THREE POINTS FOR EVERY VICTORY AND A POINT FOR ANY DRAWN BATTLES. KEEP TRACK OF THE RESULTS BY MAKING A LEAGUE TABLE. YOU COULD COMPLETE WEEKLY OR MONTHLY TABLES, DEPENDING ON HOW REGULARLY YOU PLAY. REMEMBER TO USE A PENCIL TO FILL IN THE TABLE THEN YOU CAN RUB OUT THE CONTENTS AND RE-WRITE A NEW ONE NEXT TIME.

NUMBER OF BATTLES	WINS	DRAWS

IF YOU PLAY THE SAME FRIENDS REGULARLY YOU COULD USE THESE PAGES TO PUT TOGETHER A LEAGUE TABLE TO SEE WHICH ONE OF YOU IS THE MOST SKILFUL AND SUCCESSFUL BEYBLADER.

DEFEATS	POINTS

USE THESE TWO PAGES TO KEEP TRACK OF ALL THE BATTLES YOU'VE HAD AGAINST YOUR FRIENDS. WRITE DOWN THE NAMES OF WHO YOU PLAYED AGAINST, THE BEYS YOU BOTH USED, THE RESULTS AND ANY MEMORABLE MOMENTS AND MOVES.

WHO WON?

HOW DID THE BATTLE END?

ANY MEMORABLE MOMENTS?

Jot down any techniques or tips that you've learned during battle and any future tactics and strategies you plan to use.

QUICK ACTIVITY

Who am I?
Clue: My Beyblade is Flame Sagittario, Gingka is my friend and I'm friends with Madoka.

Answer:

THE WOLF'S AMBITION

Kyoya, Benkei and some of the Face Hunters were flying in a helicopter but they didn't know where they were heading!

Pegasus' repair work. She gave the Bey a final scan to check it was ok before returning it. Kenta burst in, begging Gingka to teach him to become a top Beyblader.

They landed in a rocky, barren desert-like landscape where they were greeted by a man in a suit. He said he wanted to help Kyoya become even more powerful and was determined to see Gingka defeated.
"I thought you'd be tired of losing," he said.
"Don't you want to shake things up a bit? I will do all I can to help you win."

Back in town, Gingka was at Madoka's workshop, as she put the finishing touches to

"I need to be stronger, Gingka," he said.
"That's why I need to be trained by you and only you."
Gingka hesitated but then three of Kenta's friends entered the workshop, also demanding training.
Madoka was not amused. "Does this look like a battlefield to you?" she shouted. "If you want to battle go to Bey Park."

They all headed off for Bey Park as Kenta and his friends continued to plead with Gingka to train them. Gingka made his excuses and ran off.

about his defeat to Gingka and accused him of running away.
"How dare you, I never run away," Kyoya replied. "I will defeat him. This battle is between me and Gingka."

Kyoya and the Face Hunters were still talking to the mysterious man who explained that he was not a fan of Gingka.
"If you work with us and be a good boy, you might actually get to hear the whole story," he told Kyoya.

But the suited man wasn't about to give up and suggested Kyoya was a loser and needed his help.
"I could make you a winner," the stranger announced. "Just zip it and do as I say." This angered Kyoya. "Who do you think you are? I don't take orders."

The man told Kyoya that he had potential and with his help could one day be good enough to win a battle against Gingka. It became clear that the only one way to settle this argument was with a Beyblade battle. Kyoya agreed that if he lost he would listen to the stranger. But first, Benkei and some of the other Face Hunters decided they wanted to battle.

Kyoya wasn't pleased. He felt like the man was wasting his time and started to walk off with the other Face Hunters. They stopped in their tracks when the man mocked Kyoya

"Ok, eat Beyblade boys!" said the stranger as he launched his Bey. In no time at all his Bey had scattered the other Beys all over the floor. His Dark Wolf had proved too tough an opponent.

Benkei knew this was the ultimate Balance Type Beyblade, with equal levels of attack, defence and stamina.

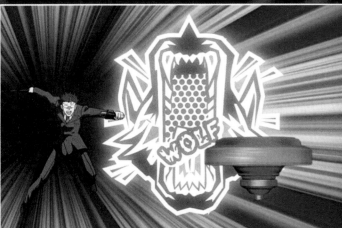

Next up, it was Kyoya. "We'll see how ultimate that thing is," he said as he prepared Rock Leone for battle.

Back in town Kenta and his friends were battling with their Beys but remained disappointed at Gingka's reluctance to train them.

Kenta decided he and his friends weren't worthy competition for Gingka and worried that his new friend might soon leave town for further challenges.

Meanwhile, Kyoya's battle was lasting a lot longer as both Beys met the challenge. The Dark Wolf's balance powers make it a harder target to hit, but Kyoya was confident it didn't have the necessary attacking powers to defeat Rock Leone.

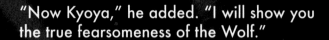

Kyoya decided to use one of his special moves, Lion Gale-Force Wall, which whipped up a whirlwind that surrounded his Bey. "That should be an impressive defence technique but when I see it, it just looks like a lion trapped in a cage," the stranger mocked.

"Don't make the mistake of thinking Leone only has defensive skills," Kyoya warned. "Attack Leone!"
The leader of the Face Hunters unleashed Lion 100 Fang Fury, which impressed the stranger as Kyoya used the natural terrain and wind to his advantage.
"Your first mistake was bringing me here, your second was underestimating me and my Leone," he laughed.
"Really, I just want to know one thing," replied the stranger. "Is that all you've got?"
He revealed he'd chosen the location to give Kyoya an advantage as he was such a weak opponent.

"Now Kyoya," he added. "I will show you the true fearsomeness of the Wolf."

Meanwhile, Gingka was alone and contemplating the requests for coaching, when Kenta approached.
"Hey Gingka, I have a request for you," he said.
"Sorry Kenta, I can't really coach," Gingka replied.
Kenta demanded a man-to-man battle to prove himself to Gingka.

Gingka reluctantly agreed and decided he wouldn't go easy on his young friend. Kenta hoped he could win or at least make it

an even match to ensure that Gingka saw him as a worthy opponent.
After what appeared to be a miss-shoot from Kenta, Gingka believed he would easily defeat his friend. Gingka encouraged Pegasus to attack.

Two strikes later and both friends were amazed that Kenta's Bey was still spinning. "The attack from Pegasus didn't finish it, what's going on here?" a puzzled Gingka asked. He realised Kenta hadn't miss-shot but that he had intended to put that much spin on Sagittario to avoid a direct hit and reduce the power of attack.

"That's not bad Kenta," praised Gingka. As the battle was taking place outside and

not in a stadium both friends knew that the competition would be decided by which Beyblade stopped first. Kenta's Stamina Type Bey had a good chance of winning. "The only way a Stamina Type like Sagittario can win is to create a drawn-out battle," said Kenta. "You can do it Sagittario, don't give up!"

Kyoya was also still deep in battle and Benkei realised the stranger's Bey was on top, using the wind created by Kyoya's Rock Leone to increase its own speed as it prepared for an attack.

"Brace youselves gentlemen," the stranger warned. "This is Dark Wolf's special move... Darkness Howling Blazer!"

The Dark Wolf Bey sliced through the whirlwind before knocking Rock Leone upside down and out of the battle.

"That's so twisted," grunted a dejected Kyoya before asking why the stranger wasn't willing to battle Gingka himself.

His only reply was that Kyoya must keep the promise he made.

With one battle over, the other was approaching its climax as Gingka and Kenta's Beys spun away with purpose. Gingka saw that Pegasus was running out of stamina and plotted one final attack at Sagittario. It didn't work and Kenta sensed victory as his Bey knocked Pegasus flying into the air.

"Alright, Sagittario beat Pegasus," he shouted.

"Not so fast Kenta," replied Gingka as Pegasus appeared high in the sky ready for the Starblast Attack. Sagittario and Kenta were defeated.
A deflated Kenta was consoled by his friend.

"You did great Kenta," Gingka said. "Luckily I still had my special move left at the end. That's the only thing that let me win the battle."
"But if I lost then there was no point," replied Kenta. "If there are no strong opponents, you will just go off somewhere else again and I don't want that."
Kenta pleaded with Gingka and promised he'd get stronger and be a worthy competitor. But Gingka explained he wasn't thinking of leaving town.
Kenta still didn't understand why Gingka wouldn't train him and his friends.

"Listen Kenta, with Beyblade you just can't be taught how to become any stronger. The Bey's strength is decided right here," Gingka replied, pointing to his heart.
Gingka said if they continued to have similar battles he would be more than happy to stay and was pleased to be around somebody who wanted to win so much.

Will Benkei have both of those questions answered soon? Turn to page 62.

"Thanks to you, I've managed to find another rival that gets my spirit up," Gingka said as they agree to battle again, man-to-man.

As the Face Hunters trudged back to their hideout they wondered where Kyoya had gone. "There's nothing to do," said Benkei. "Kyoya lost the battle so he has to listen to that guy, so we just have to wait for him to contact us, but I'd still like to know who that guy is and where he's taken Kyoya."

SECRET SERVICE

DURING THE LAST STORY WE MET A MYSTERIOUS STRANGER FOR THE FIRST TIME. AS THE OBSERVANT BEYBLADERS AMONGST YOU WILL HAVE NOTICED FROM THE OTHER PAGES IN THE ANNUAL. THE STRANGER'S NAME IS DOJI. AT FIRST HE KEEPS HIS NAME SECRET BUT CAN YOU FIND OUT WHAT ORGANISATION HE IS AN EXECUTIVE OF BY FILLING IN THE CLUES FROM THE FOLLOWING QUESTIONS?

1.
2.
3.
4.
5.
6.
7.
8.
9.
10.

QUESTIONS:

1. Who gets annoyed when Kenta and his friends battle in her workshop? (6 letters)
2. Who battles against a mysterious stranger in the desert? (5 letters)
3/8. What is the name of Gingka's Beyblade? (5 letters and 7 letters)
4. Which Face Hunter decides he wants to battle the mysterious stranger before he takes on Kyoya? (6 letters)
5. Who is reluctant to coach Kenta? (6 letters)
6. The what Hunters are lead by Kyoya? (4 letters)
7. The Dark Wolf's special move is called the Darkness Howling . . . . what? (4 letters)
8. See question 3.
9. Kyoya's defeated Bey is known as Rock . . . . what? (5 letters)
10. Who realises that the only way of learning from Gingka is to battle him? (5 letters)

QUICK ACTIVITY

Who am I?
Clue: I am a Beyblade mechanic but I rarely battle and I have my own Bey workshop.

Answer:

ANSWERS ON PAGE 78

54

CAPTURE THE ACTION

GINGKA

CHECK OUT THIS COOL DRAWING OF GINGKA ABOUT TO LAUNCH STORM PEGASUS INTO ACTION. TRY TO DRAW YOUR OWN VERSION IN THE SECOND BLANK GRID, USING THE FIRST GRID AS A GUIDE.

QUICK ACTIVITY

Who am I?
Clue: I am the original owner of the Bey Pegasus.

Answer:

GINGKA

DRAW YOUR PICTURE HERE

TOP TIPS

TO GET THE MOST OUT OF YOUR BEYBLADE TOP HAVE A WHIZ THROUGH THESE TOP TIPS...

KNOW YOUR BEYBLADE

Make sure you understand and are used to...
- Its launch rip speed
- The timing, angle and direction of its release
- The position and style of its launch-landing within the Beystadium arena.
- Its battle path & special moves.

BREAK IN YOUR GEAR

Don't always expect a brand new Beyblade top to work as well as one you've been using for a while, make sure you're prepared for battle...
- Well-used equipment often performs better. Use new spin-gear bearings and free-spinning base tips a few times before taking them into battle.
- Ripcords come tightly coiled in their original packaging and will run more smoothly after a few pulls, as will the launcher.

EXPERIMENT WITH RELEASE STYLES

Your Bey's performance largely depends on its release, with angle, flight path and landing position all affecting its battle performance. Keep the following information in mind...
- A Stamina or Defence Type is often helped by a central landing, this supports a steady spin motion.
- Landing on the sloped perimeter can help an Attack Type spiral more fiercely.

WORK ON YOUR LAUNCH

A better launch will give you a faster rip speed which will lead to an improved performance. By perfecting your launch technique you can...
- Make any attack more ferocious
- Get Attack Types to move more quickly
- Help Defence Types deflect attacks effectively
- Improve spin duration and control of Endurance Types

QUICK ACTIVITY

Who am I?
Clue: My Beyblade is Dark Wolf and has a special move called Darkness Howling Blazer.

Answer:

WHICH BENKEI?

CHECK OUT THESE TWO COOL PICTURES OF BENKEI USING HIS DARK BULL BEYBLADE TO BATTLE GINGKA'S STORM PEGASUS. AT FIRST GLANCE THE PICTURES MAY LOOK EXACTLY THE SAME BUT THERE ARE ACTUALLY SEVEN SLIGHT DIFFERENCES. CAN YOU SPOT THEM ALL?

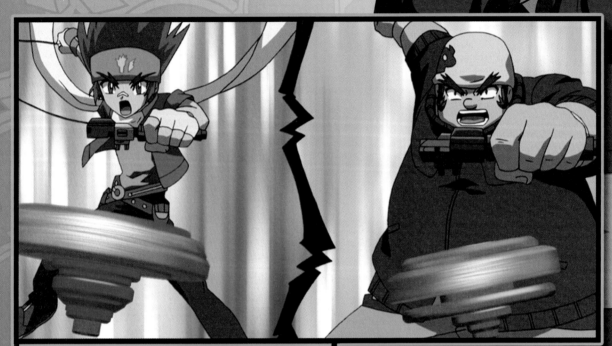

PICTURE 1

PICTURE 2

ANSWERS ON PAGE 78

POWERS OF OBSERVATION

The pictures on these pages show Gingka battling Kyoya at Metal Tower. They are being watched by Kenta, Madoka and Benkei. Concentrate on all of the details in these images and see if you can answer the tricky teasers about them on the next page.

POWERS OF OBSERVATION

1. Who is wearing sunglasses on their head?

2. Which two characters are about to launch their Beys?

3. Who is wearing a hat, a sweatband and shorts?

4. One of our heroes is missing a glove, who is it?

5. Who appears to be laughing at Kenta?

6. Who is stood next to Madoka?

7. Who has their eyes closed?

8. Who is analysing Kyoya's Beyblade?

9. What colour T-Shirt is Kenta wearing?

10. Who is wearing a white scarf?

NAME THE MOVES

How well do you know the goodies and baddies of the Beyblade Metal Fusion world? Have you been paying attention to them during their battles?

Six different Beys are pictured on this page, with six Special Moves. Simply identify which move Bey and Special move belongs to each character...

BENKEI	DOJI	RYUGA
???????	???????	???????

KYOYA	GINGKA	KENTA
???????	???????	???????

PEGASUS
STORM BRINGER

LION
100 FANG FURY

TORNADO
BULL UPPERCUT

SAGITTARIO
FLAME CLAW

DRAGON EMPEROR
SOARING BITE STRIKE

DARKNESS
HOWLING BLAZER

Gingka ran out of a fast food restaurant with a bag in his hand and a huge smile on his face.

"I got it, the triple beef burger," he shouted to a boy standing eating an ice cream.

"You don't know me, but I bet you'd like to because of the triple beef burger I'm carrying," he continued. "Kenta and Madoka are going to have serious beef envy!"

Meanwhile, Benkei was far from happy as he practised with his Beyblade inside the Face Hunters' hideout. He was thinking of Gingka and Storm Pegasus defeating Kyoya and getting angrier.

Benkei was interrupted by the stranger in the suit who had previously beaten Kyoya in battle. "You again," he said. "What have you done with Kyoya?"

The stranger reminded Benkei that, due to his defeat, Kyoya was now being put through his paces in the stranger's special training centre.

"He is learning how to maximise his powers," the stranger said. "When I deem him ready he will return and then I will have him defeat Gingka Hagane."

He told Benkei that if he wanted Kyoya back sooner he would have to defeat Gingka himself and offered him a new Bey, called Dark Bull, which specialised in upper attacks.

"With this Beyblade, Gingka will be history!" Benkei shouted.

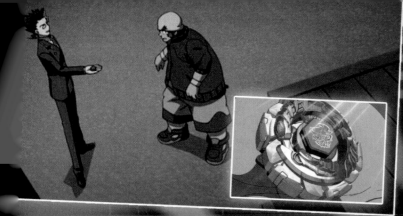

Benkei remembered the first time he came across Kyoya and how the two fought a memorable battle. Benkei had been confident of victory but Kyoya had other ideas.

"You do have power, but that's all," Kyoya shouted.
"We'll see," replied Benkei.
Rock Leone repelled Benkei's Bey, much to his amazement. Always a sore loser, he demanded a rematch. Kyoya accepted but the battle ended in the same way.
"I'm not done, I'm not done yet," Benkei protested.

"No matter how many times he falls, he keeps on getting up," Kyoya said to himself. "It's like fighting a bull."
"Thanks, I am like a bull," answered Benkei.
"And here are my horns!" he shouted as he launched his Bey into action.
After another defeat Benkei begged for another battle, but realised he'd been beaten for the first time. He was shocked that the disappointment actually felt good!

"I'm now your biggest fan," he said. "I'm going to follow you, even if you say no."
"Do whatever you want," Kyoya replied as a bond formed between two former rivals.

Inspired by the memory, Benkei was determined to help out his friend with victory over Gingka. But first he had to master his new Bey.

Kenta was battling at the Beystadium Arena with his Stamina Type, Flame Sagittario. He was up against an Attack Type and Madoka was keeping a keen eye on both Beys.

Kenta won to earn praise from his new friend. "Kenta, you're really starting to understand the unique power of Beyblades," she said.

Gingka arrived with his food bag clenched tightly in his hands. Kenta, Madoka and their friends were so caught up in their Beyblade discussions that they didn't even notice him! Gingka opened his bag, expecting to taste his triple burger but was shocked to see a hotdog and also realised that his fries were missing.

Madoka continued to show off her Bey expertise and knowledge, talking through each Bey type in great detail.

Gingka interrupted their conversation. "It's true that an understanding of how Beyblades work is important," he said. "But at the end of the day it comes down to heart."
"And good maintenance," Madoka quickly added.
"Having a heart that loves Beyblading makes a Beyblader stronger," continued Gingka.

Benkei was quickly developing his understanding of the Dark Bull Bey and defeated ten of his fellow Face Hunters' Beys in one battle, even mastering a new special move called Bull Uppercut.

Kenta and his friends were having fun in the park when Benkei crashed their party.
"What do you want from us?" Kenta asked nervously.

"My business isn't with you, kid," Benkei roared. "Tell Gingka I'm challenging him to a battle."

They informed Gingka and Madoka advised they had nothing further to do with the Face Hunters. Gingka disagreed.
"If I don't show up they'll come looking for me," he said. "They mean business."

Kenta noticed a bull-shaped hole in a nearby crate and the three friends found further similar shaped holes as they got closer to the Face Hunters' hideout. They realised the holes had been made by a Beyblade.
"Talk about an awesome force," said Gingka as he chased after the spinning Bey and entered the warehouse to find Benkei.

"I've been waiting for you, Gingka," he growled. He explained that he had made the bull-shaped holes while training to defeat Gingka.
"No matter what, you're going down," Benkei shouted.
"Wow, this is awesome. I am so pumped," Gingka replied.

Benkei was surprised by his rivals' reaction and announced the commencement of battle. "3,2,1... Let it rip!" they both shouted as the Beys whizzed through the air.

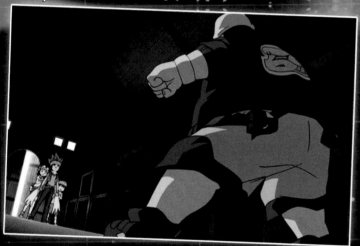

Madoka began to analyse Benkei's Dark Bull Bey and admitted she'd never seen a Beyblade like it before. She speculated that it was a Balance Type.

Everybody was surprised when the Dark Bull Bey pushed Gingka's Pegasus back. Benkei reminded himself not to be impatient and to wait for his chance to attack. When it came he went with his new special move, shouting, "Strike! Bull Uppercut!"

Madoka continued to study the battle and Benkei's new Bey. She explained to Kenta how Dark Bull's performance tip was causing Pegasus problems.
Gingka again fought back, much to the annoyance of Benkei.
"You're good," he said. "That's why defeating you is going to be sweet."
The power caused by the super fast rotation of both Beys almost led to danger for Madoka and Kenta as a crate was blown towards them.

Gingka pleaded for Pegasus to save his friends and his Bey quickly obliged, knocking the crate clear.
But the danger wasn't over as the ceiling and several large wooden beams crashed to the ground looking as though they would crush Gingka...

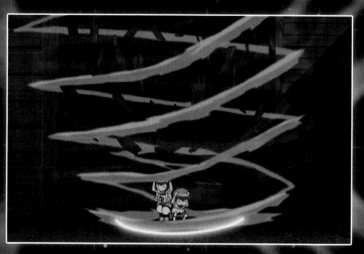

An unlikely hero came to his rescue as Benkei dived through the air to push Gingka away to safety. Everyone in the room was shocked.

As the battle continued, with Pegasus and Dark Bull going head-to-head, it was unclear which Bey and which Beyblader would be victorious. Benkei sensed glory after performing his Bull Uppercut move, but Gingka had other ideas, performing a special move of his own with the Pegasus Starblast Attack.
The move crushed Dark Bull into the ground and ensured Gingka was triumphant.
"Oh man, that was so much fun!" Gingka said to Benkei.

"Your Bull Uppercut was a great technique," Gingka added, stretching out his hand to Benkei. The Face Hunter rejected Gingka's handshake and offer of friendship.

"Benkei, you saved me," Gingka said.
"No I didn't," replied Benkei. "You just keep battling!"

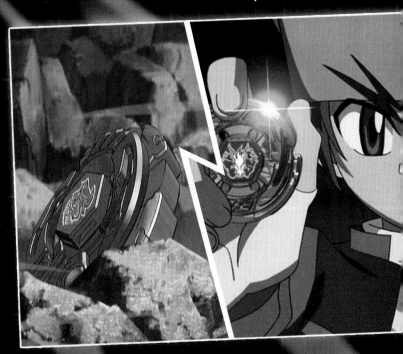

To celebrate, Gingka, Madoka and Kenta headed back to the fast food restaurant where Gingka finally got his hands on a triple beef burger.

"Yum, hotdogs are for losers, burgers are for winners!" he shouted.
Madoka appeared quiet. She thought it was strange that Benkei, a Face Hunter that would do whatever it took to win, chose to save Gingka from danger.

Kenta agreed – but Gingka had his own theory.
"He probably just wanted a real fight because he trained so hard. Maybe he didn't want to cheat after putting all of that effort

into training his new Bey. He wanted to win fair and square, that's all," explained Ginga. Benkei sat on the other side of the restaurant angrily tucking into a pile of burgers and questioning himself for saving Gingka.

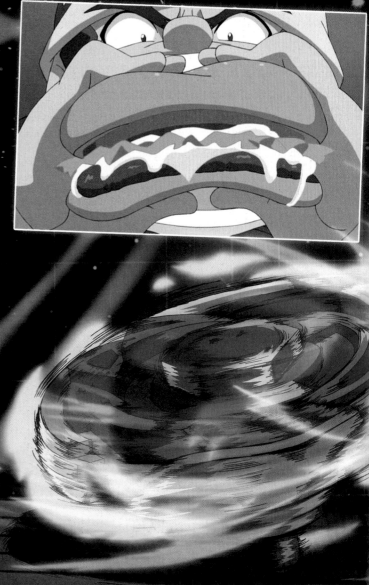

CHARGE!
BULL
POWER!

BLADER BATTLE

There are two battles taking place here. One is between Gingka and Kenta and one between Kyoya and Doji. Join up the dots to see who is winning...

Now add a splash of colour!
When you have completed the drawing get out your crayons or coloured pencils and see if you can make the scene really come to life with some bright colours!

TRUE OR FALSE?

BY NOW YOU SHOULD HAVE BUILT UP A GOOD BEYBLADE KNOWLEDGE FROM READING THIS ANNUAL AND COMPLETING THE ACTIVITIES. BUT THIS TRUE OF FALSE QUIZ COULD BE A REAL TEST OF YOUR BEYBLADE BRAIN. READ THROUGH THESE 20 STATEMENTS AND WORK OUT WHICH ONES ARE TRUE AND WHICH ARE FALSE...

QUESTION 1:

Kyoya was once leader of the Face Hunters.

☐ TRUE ☐ FALSE

QUESTION 2:

Doji uses a Beyblade called Bright Fox.

☐ TRUE ☐ FALSE

QUESTION 3:

Madoka's special move is the Mechanical Whirl.

☐ TRUE ☐ FALSE

QUESTION 4:

Kenta shows Gingka the strength of friendship.

☐ TRUE ☐ FALSE

QUESTION 5:

Dark Nebula are the evil group targeting Gingka.

☐ TRUE ☐ FALSE

QUESTION 6:

The Lightning L-Drago Beyblade belongs to Doji.

☐ TRUE ☐ FALSE

QUESTION 7:

Kyoya is one of the good guys.

☐ TRUE ☐ FALSE

QUESTION 8:

One of Benkei's special moves is the Bull Uppercut.

☐ TRUE ☐ FALSE

72

QUESTION 9:

Many of Kenta's battles take place at the Beystadium Arena.

☐ TRUE ☐ FALSE

QUESTION 10:

Kyoya's Beyblade is called Stone Treona.

☐ TRUE ☐ FALSE

QUESTION 11:

Kyoya and Benkei are enemies.

☐ TRUE ☐ FALSE

QUESTION 12:

Kyoya uses King Lion Tearing Blast.

☐ TRUE ☐ FALSE

QUESTION 13:

Teru used to be a talented dancer.

☐ TRUE ☐ FALSE

QUESTION 14:

Doji plans to destroy Gingka.

☐ TRUE ☐ FALSE

QUESTION 15:

Madoka's Beyblade is called Mega Spin.

☐ TRUE ☐ FALSE

QUESTION 16:

Ryo is Gingka's father.

☐ TRUE ☐ FALSE

QUESTION 17:

The Sagittario Flame Claw belongs to Hyoma.

☐ TRUE ☐ FALSE

QUESTION 18:

Like Kyoya, Benkei started off as a Face Hunter.

☐ TRUE ☐ FALSE

QUESTION 19:

Kenta seeks Gingka's mentorship after seeing him in battle.

☐ TRUE ☐ FALSE

QUESTION 20:

Gingka's Beyblade is the Storm Pegasus.

☐ TRUE ☐ FALSE

ANSWERS ON PAGE 78

BRIGHTEN THE BEYBLADES

Kyoya and Gingka are battling inside a futuristic blue Beystadium. Use the colour key below as a guide and try to colour each section in correctly to bring this picture to life...

| 1 | 2 | 3 | 4 | 5 | 6 | 7 | 8 | 9 | 10 | 11 |

FILL IN THE BLANKS

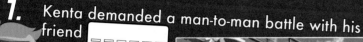

1. Kenta demanded a man-to-man battle with his friend `_ _ _ _ _ _`

2. Gingka realised that if he doesn't give his all, it will be disrespectful to Kenta so he put extra effort into achieving victory, encouraging his `_ _ _ _ _ _ _ _` Bey to attack.

3. With the battle taking place outside – not in a stadium – both friends knew the competition was to see whose Beyblade would stop first, meaning Kenta's `_ _ _ _ _ _ _` Type had a good chance of winning.

4. "The only way my `_ _ _ _ _ _ _ _` Bey can win is to create a drawn-out battle," said Kenta.

5. Kenta sensed victory as his Bey knocked Pegasus flying into the air. "Alright, my Sagittario beat Pegasus," he shouted.
"Not so fast Kenta," replied Gingka as Pegasus appeared high in the sky ready for the `_ _ _ _ _ _ _` Attack, which left Kenta defeated.

WHO SAID THAT?

AFTER READING THE FOUR STORIES YOU'LL NOW KNOW QUITE A LOT ABOUT MOST OF THE BEYBLADE CHARACTERS. NOW IT'S TIME TO PUT YOUR KNOWLEDGE TO THE TEST. READ THE QUOTES BELOW AND DECIDE WHICH OF THE CHARACTERS IS MOST LIKELY TO HAVE SAID EACH ONE...

QUESTION 1:
"A true Beyblader uses their heart to succeed during battle."
Answer:

QUESTION 2:
"I am like a bull and here are my horns!"
Answer:

QUESTION 3:
"Brace yourselves gentlemen, this is Dark Wolf's special move... Darkness Howling Blazer!"
Answer:

QUESTION 4:
"You can do it Sagittario, don't give up!"
Answer:

QUESTION 5:
"Your first mistake was bringing me here, your second was underestimating me and my Leone."
Answer:

QUESTION 6:
"Pegasus Star Blast Attack!"
Answer:

QUESTION 7:
I still haven't finished Pegasus's maintenance yet. I have to fine tune its balance."
Answer:

QUESTION 8:
"What are you doing you Face Stealing monster? Give me my Sagittario back!"
Answer:

QUESTION 9:
"The difference between winning and losing is the Bey's spirit."
Answer:

QUESTION 10:
"Gingka Hagane must be destroyed."
Answer:

ANSWERS ON PAGE 78

DESIGN YOUR OWN
BEYBLADE

THINK OF YOUR FAVOURITE BEYBLADE TOPS AND TRY TO DESIGN YOUR OWN SPECIALLY MODIFIED TOP. CONSIDER THE COLOUR, LOOK AND SPECIAL FEATURES OF YOUR BEYBLADE. LOOK AT THE PICTURES OF EXISTING BEY'S AND SEE WHAT YOU CAN COME UP WITH.

ANSWERS:

Pages 22/23
MEMORY QUIZ
1. The WBBA competition
2. Flame Sagittario or Sagittario for short
3. Top eight
4. Benkei
5. Gingka
6. Hagane
7. Five
8. Rock Leone or Leone for short
9. 100
10. The Beyblader's spirit

Page 25
BUMPER BEYBLADE WORDSEARCH

N	B	E	N	Y	I	O	L	I	S	O	G	A
P	G	O	Z	U	R	G	J	J	N	B	C	Q
E	I	G	V	J	K	O	O	P	O	E	C	B
O	N	X	Z	S	D	A	Y	O	Y	K	S	E
B	G	T	S	J	K	B	L	P	W	T	A	N
R	K	V	H	O	K	U	T	O	W	O	U	K
O	A	B	H	K	I	U	A	Y	U	F	C	E
A	A	A	S	A	B	U	S	T	J	U	S	I
Z	J	V	F	G	Y	T	T	S	N	L	A	S
O	B	N	K	I	D	F	Y	Z	K	E	N	G
T	Y	S	J	F	T	O	B	I	O	G	K	A
E	P	R	W	O	C	G	S	O	X	Z	G	F
A	M	Y	G	R	F	C	X	S	O	U	Z	A
U	K	A	M	O	Y	H	T	E	Y	R	R	R
L	C	F	G	J	N	S	O	R	A	W	O	O
R	M	A	D	O	K	A	O	L	I	M	O	S

Pages 26/27
MEGA MAZE

Page 28
BEYBLADE MATCH UP
GINGKA : Storm Pegasus
KYOYA : Rock Leone
BENKEI : Dark Bull
KENTA : Flame Sagittario
RYUGA : Lightening L-Drago
DOJI : Dark Wolf

Page 41
MIXED-UP CHARACTERS
KANGIG : GINGKA
TENKA : KENTA
JODI : DOJI
OBOIT : TOBIO
AROS : SORA
YAKYO : KYOYA
KAMADO : MADOKA
ENEKBI : BENKEI

Pages 42/43
BEY BRAIN TEASER
1. Storm Pegasus
2. Either... Lion Gale-force Wall,
   Lion 100 Fang Fury,
   Lion Wild Wind Fang Dance or
   King Lion Tearing Blast
3. Teru
4. Ryuga
5. Madoka
6. Gingka
7. Hyoma
8. Dark Bull
9. Nebula
10. Hokuto
11. Kyoya
12. Ryo
13. Ryuga
14. Dan
15. Sagittario Flame Claw
16. Either... Pegasus Starblast Attack,
    Pegasus Tornado Wing,
    Meteor Shower Attack or
    Pegasus Storm Bringer
17. Doji
18. Green
19. Tetsuya Watarigani
20. Ryuga